Piggyback

by David Robert Burleigh

Illustrated by Ben Abril

FOLLETT PUBLISHING COMPANY

Chicago

1055

TLA 7035

THIRD PRINTING

Library of Congress Catalog Card Number: 62-15674

Little children sometimes ride piggyback
on their father's shoulders.

This book is the story of trucks riding
piggyback on trains.

Long ago there was a piggyback train when the circus came to town.

The circus wagons were carried on flatcars—piggyback.

Early in the morning a puffing steam engine shoved the circus train against an unloading ramp.

Horses pulled the wagons along the flatcars and down the ramp.

Elephants were there, pushing and pulling too.

The animal cages, the band wagon, and the calliope were lined up for the parade.

The heavy wagons, carrying the Big Top and the other tents, rolled to the circus grounds.

What excitement! The circus was in town.

On the last day of the circus, while the night
show was going on under the Big Top and all the
people were watching the clowns and acrobats, the
sideshow tents were coming down.

The animal cages were already gone.

They were rolling through the darkness to the
train of flatcars waiting at the railroad tracks.

Once more the elephants were shuffling along, hard at work, pulling the circus wagons up the ramp and along the flatcars to their regular places.

As soon as the circus train was loaded, the engine roared away as fast as it could go.

The circus had to be in another town at daybreak.

Many years later a railroad man asked,

"Why don't we carry trucks the way we used to carry circus wagons? If the trucks were loaded in the afternoon, fast trains could take them to another city during the night."

So they did.

They began to carry truck-trailers on flatcars.

Here is a yellow trailer which is going on a
piggyback trip from Los Angeles to San Francisco.

It is being loaded with an important shipment
which must be in San Francisco tomorrow morning.

This tractor, which is often called the cab, has come to get the yellow trailer.

Its driver is in a hurry to take the trailer to the railroad yards.

The Zipper, the fast freight train which carries the piggybacks, will soon be leaving.

The tractor swings around and backs against
the trailer.

The tractor slot slides back to the knob on the
trailer.

The plate lifts the trailer off its dolly wheels.

Then the air hoses are hooked together.

The coupling is made very quickly.

The tractor pulls the trailer through the city.

Then it turns down a narrow street, bumps over many railroad tracks, and swings into a wide lot.

This is the railroad piggyback loading yard.

A great many trailers are lined up waiting to get on the piggyback train.

The tractor shoves the trailer backwards up a cement slope.

As the trailer rolls off the ramp, its rear axle slides along two steel beams that run down the middle of the flatcar.

The moment the trailer stops, a man at the side of the car turns a big crank.

This brings two steel clamps up between the steel beams to hook on to the trailer's rear axle.

The tractor goes away, leaving the yellow trailer tightly clamped to the flatcar.

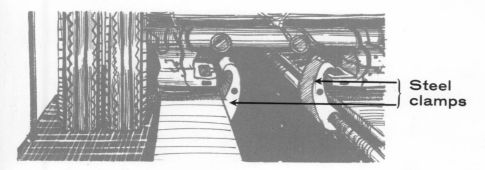

Steel clamps

"Is that yellow trailer tied down?" calls a railroad switchman.

"It's tight," answers the man who turned the crank. "You can take them away."

A switch engine couples to the row of loaded flatcars and pulls them away from the loading ramp.

The switchman throws a switch at the end of the truck.

Then he signals the switch engine to shove the loaded cars into another long track.

This is the Zipper's make-up track.

As fast as the trailers are loaded, the switch engine pulls the flatcars out of the loading tracks and shoves them against the cars already in the long make-up track.

When all the piggyback cars have been shoved together, the silver-colored caboose is coupled at the rear.

The Zipper is made up, ready for its engine.

The road engine is already waiting a few feet in front of the train.

It looks like a short train all by itself, for it has three diesel engines coupled together.

"S-s-s-s-s."

That is the hiss of air through brake pipes.

The engineer is testing the air brakes.

The conductor gives the engineer a copy of the orders.

The Zipper is ready to start.

With a low roar the engine begins to move—slowly, at first, to let the conductor and the swing brakeman "roll the train."

They stand beside the slowly moving train checking wheels and brakes.

They make sure all the trailers are tightly clamped on the flatcars.

The moment they swing onto the caboose, the rear brakeman uses the radio-telephone to call to the engineer:

"Everybody on! Highball!"

The engine leaps ahead, up the river, under railroad bridges and highway overpasses, past a switch tower, out to the high-speed' main line.

Though the Zipper is still in the city, beside a crowded street, it can race forward at full speed.

At the road crossings the gates are down, holding back the autos and trucks.

The piggybacks are streaking north, toward green signals blinking in the distance.

Cars on the highway are often stopped by red signals at intersections.

But the signals ahead of the Zipper keep flashing green.

They are railroad signals, which turn green whenever there is no train on the track ahead.

And there is no train ahead.

All the freight trains have received orders to get off the main line and wait in the sidings.

The "high iron" belongs to the "hotshot."

The Zipper flashes through the San Fernando Valley.

Then, Whoosh! The engine dives into a mountain.

All the trailers follow.

One after another they plunge into the black tunnel, filled with the thunder of diesel motors at full throttle.

The whole train of seventy flatcars disappears, for this tunnel is over a mile along.

It is getting dark by the time the engine
pokes its nose out at the other end of the tunnel.

But the engine's blazing headlight leaps
ahead to find the two shiny rails.

It swings around curves to light up the orange
groves and walnut orchards.

The engineer is not racing trucks on the highway now.

They have all been left far behind.

He is racing against time—for the Zipper is due at Santa Barbara at nine-thirty.

The piggyback train roars along the beach, and then swings inland to a tree-shaded valley.

Here is the old mission city beside the Pacific Ocean.

The time is exactly nine-thirty.

At Santa Barbara a fresh crew takes charge.

The new engineer leans out of the cab window, a brakeman waves his lantern, and the train starts moving.

It doesn't take long for the new brakemen to "roll the train" and swing onto the caboose.

"Highball," shouts the conductor over the radio-telephone.

"Highball," repeats the engineer as he pulls the throttle to the last notch.

The piggybacks are on the way again— rocketing along the shores of the Pacific Ocean.

Clickety-clickety-click.

Through sleeping towns and quiet cities the Zipper races north.

Once, however, it leaves the main line.

In the middle of the night, on the edge of a canyon in the Santa Lucia Mountains, the piggybacks stop in a siding.

A few moments later a gleaming headlight swings around the curve and the southbound passenger train streaks past.

Once more on the "high rail" the Zipper roars ahead, through King City and Salinas, Watsonville and San Jose.

North of San Jose the engineer and fireman have to keep sharp eyes ahead.

The signals are blinking yellow—and RED.

The piggybacks are following one of the commuter trains. These are passenger trains which take people from their homes in the suburbs to their offices in San Francisco.

At every town people are waiting. Palo Alto, San Mateo, Burlingame are names on the stations.

Many of these people hurried away from home without breakfast. There is a coffee shop at the station where they can eat before catching a train.

They can watch the piggyback roll by while they eat. The Zipper engine toots a good morning; the commuters, with a cup of coffee in one hand, wave a cheery reply with the other.

As the Zipper nears the city with its great Bay bridge, it has to reduce speed.

The piggyback train has to find its way through a twisted tangle of tracks between factories and warehouses.

Then it rolls through a short tunnel, swings around a curve, and pulls to a stop.

The road engine has completed its long night's work.

It has brought the piggybacks into San Francisco on time.

A switch engine ducks in behind the train and begins to cut it up.

It pulls some of the piggyback cars back and then shoves them into an unloading spur.

A second and third "cut" go into a second and third track.

Then the car with the yellow trailer moves toward the back of the unloading ramp.

As soon as the flatcar nudges into the low cement wall, a tractor backs up the ramp, rolls on to the flatcar, and grabs the yellow trailer.

The piggyback trip is over.

The big yellow trailer rolls through the streets of San Francisco to a great hospital.

There, on a platform at the rear, men are waiting to unload it.

For it is filled with supplies for nurses and doctors; medicines and drugs for the sick people in the hospital; vaccines and "shots" to keep children well.

That is the "rush" shipment the yellow trailer carries.

That was why it came piggyback—on the Los Angeles–San Francisco Fast Freight.

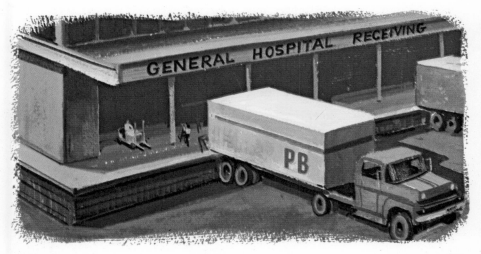

Another piggyback train is called Tructrain.

It starts in New York with a parade of truck-trailers which rumble through a tunnel under the Hudson River to the railroad yards.

This train starts at midnight and races across New Jersey to Philadelphia, where more trailers wait to go with it.

Across the mountains of Pennsylvania the "hotshot" speeds.

At Pittsburgh it stops long enough to switch some of its trailers to a fast freight bound for Toledo and Detroit.

Then it races through Ohio and Indiana to Chicago, arriving there 25 hours after leaving New York.

Trailers are carried piggyback between many other cities.

They go from Omaha to New York; St. Louis to New Orleans; Kansas City to Dallas; Chicago to Minneapolis; Cleveland to Baltimore.

Many of these shipments are overnight, like the trip of the yellow trailer.

Other piggyback shipments travel two or three days to reach their destination.

Follett Beginning Social Studies Books

Follett Beginning Social Studies books contain accurate, up-to-date information about our world—its history and geography, its people and their ways of life. These books are designed to provide pleasure in reading and to give children the information they need to enrich their lives and their school work.

Follett Beginning Social Studies books are written for the primary grades. They are completely illustrated. They cover a wide range of subjects, adding interest to the familiar and shedding light on the unfamiliar.

Piggyback

Understandings Developed in This Book

Men often adapt an idea for use in other ways.

Circuses used flatcars to move the circus wagons overnight from town to town. Railroad men later took up the idea and began to move loaded trucks on trains.

Men use many different inventions and work together to make the piggyback trip fast and efficient.

Machinery

Tractors and trailers, air hoses for coupling, ramps leading to flatcar, clamps on flatcar to hold trailer, radio-telephone.

Workers

Truck driver, switchmen, conductor, engineer, brakemen.

Organization

Trains run on regular schedules. Gates hold back cars and trucks at crossings. All freight trains get off the main line and wait till the piggyback passes. A system of signals helps railroad men to work together quickly and safely and well.

Words That May Be New

(Note: To add interest and authenticity to this story of a piggyback train, the author has used many geographical names. These are not in the word list below. It is suggested that the places named in the text be located on a map by the teacher or parent and children, both as a means of solving the reading problem they may present and to add to the children's interest in the story and in the use of maps.)

acrobats	caboose	rocketing	tangle
sideshow	diesel	canyon	warehouse
shuffling	overpasses	gleaming	unloading
trailer	blinking	headlight	spur
coupling	intersections	southbound	nudges
crank	sidings	streaks	hospital
clamps	tunnel	commuter	vaccines
axle	blazing	reduce	Tructrain
switch	mission	twisted	destination